T0084445

— **EULENBURG AUDIO+SCORE**

Ludwig van Beethoven

Symphony No. 4 in B♭ major / B-Dur

Op. 60

Edited by / Herausgegeben von
Richard Clarke

EULENBURG

EAS 187
ISBN 978-3-7957-6587-3
ISMN 979-0-2002-2617-1

© 2014 Ernst Eulenburg & Co GmbH, Mainz
for Europe excluding the British Isles
Ernst Eulenburg Ltd, London
for all other countries
CD ℗ 1997 NAXOS Rights US, Inc.
CD © 2014 Ernst Eulenburg Ltd, London

Ernst Eulenburg Ltd
48 Great Marlborough Street
London W1F 7BB

Contents / Inhalt

Allegro vivace

Trio. Un poco meno Allegro

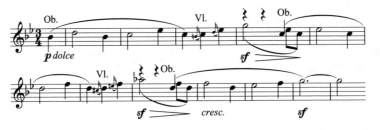

Preface

Dedicated to Count Franz von Oppersdorf
Composed: 1806 in Vienna
First performance: March 1807 in the apartment of Prince Lobkowitz;
first public performance on 15 November 1807 at the Burgtheater of Vienna
Original publisher: Bureau des Arts et d'Industrie, Vienna and Pest, 1809;
first score published by Simrock, 1823
Instrumentation: Flute, 2 Oboes, 2 Clarinets, 2 Bassoons – 2 Horns,
2 Trumpets – Timpani – Strings
Duration: ca. 35 minutes

Beethoven composed his Fourth Symphony during a period of exceptional productivity. Having finished the *Eroica* Symphony (No.3) in 1804, he soon began jotting down ideas for what were to become his Fifth (C minor) and Sixth (*Pastoral*) symphonies. But Beethoven seems to have realized that these seeds would need time to germinate. Where most composers would have turned their attentions to something less demanding, Beethoven decided to occupy his mind with another symphony. The resulting work, published in 1808 as Symphony No.4 in B flat major, appears to have emerged rapidly, probably during July-August 1806 – that is, during a break in the composition of the three 'Razumovsky' Quartets, Op.59. In marked contrast to Symphonies 3, 5 and 6, all of which were sketched extensively, hardly any sketches have survived for Symphony No.4, which has led some Beethoven authorities to conclude that Beethoven began working on the full score almost immediately.[1]

The Fourth Symphony's comparatively easy conception and birth have led to a widespread belief that it represents a relaxation, even a regression, after the audacious originality of the *Eroica*. A superficial glance at the score would tend to bear this out. Where the Third and Fifth symphonies enhanced the expressive power of the early 19th-century orchestra as never before, the Fourth seems on the whole more classical in manner. It is scored for the smallest orchestra Beethoven ever employed in a symphony: just one flute, pairs of oboes, clarinets, bassoons, horns, trumpets and drums, plus the usual strings. The *Eroica* and C minor symphonies both feature bold formal innovations: the fusion of variation and sonata form in the finale of the *Eroica* for instance, or the superb cumulative transition between scherzo and finale in the Fifth Symphony. The Fourth, on the other hand, seems largely content with inherited classical procedures.

---

[1] See for instance, Barry Cooper, Introduction to Beethoven Symphony No.4 (Kassel, etc., 2001), iii

VI

Look deeper, however, and the Fourth Symphony's originality and sophistication become clear. The Beethoven-scholar Lewis Lockwood has praised this symphony's 'godlike play among delicately poised forces',[2] the composer Robert Schumann called it 'the Greek-like slender one'.[3] Like the Fifth Symphony, the Fourth charts a darkness-to-light course, though here the thrilling emergence into sunlight emerges much earlier. The slow introduction is in the sombre key of B flat minor. First comes a sustained, hushed multi-octave unison (wind), with slow falling thirds on strings. This is heard twice, after which tentative violin figures grope in new tonal directions (b18, etc.). Then the violins repeat just one note, *crescendo* (b35), and a blazing repeated *fortissimo* gesture from the whole orchestra sweeps us straight into the *Allegro vivace* and the major key.

Darkness dispelled, the 'godlike play' begins. Something of the conversational spirit of classical chamber music enters the writing in the first movement, with lively dialogues amongst or between the woodwind and string sections. The most original stroke comes just before the return of the *Allegro*'s first theme. The energetic development section seems to become impaled on a dissonant chord (b261), which then breaks down into hushed fragments on alternating first and second violins: first *staccato*, then *legato*. This settles into a seventh chord of F sharp major (b281) marked *ppp* – an extreme dynamic for its time. The timpani, however, quietly insist on B flat (enharmonically A sharp, the third of F sharp). The strings' harmony then shifts to B flat major, tonic 6-4 (b305), and a long *crescendo* leads to the return of the first theme in triumph (b337).

Much of the drama in the Fourth's Symphony's *Adagio* stems from the interaction and contrast between songlike melody and martial rhythms. The march element makes its presence felt at once, on second violins with a sharply memorable dotted rhythm on two notes. The long-breathed first violin melody that follows doesn't banish the memory of this rhythm (hints of it persist in the lower strings); then at the melody's climax it erupts again, now underlined forcefully by trumpets and timpani (b9). At the heart of the *Adagio* comes an especially poetic moment. After the movement's anguished central climax, violins seem to become stuck on a single ambiguous quiet chord (b54ff.) – as in the remarkable hushed passage at the heart of the first movement. The martial figure flickers on high bassoon, a clarinet laments softly – then comes another 'sunlight' moment as horns, timpani and flute steer the movement effortlessly into the recapitulation (b64).

There is one clear innovation in the following scherzo: instead of the classical A–B–A formal pattern (inherited from the Minuet), Beethoven takes us on a circular A–B–A–B–A journey, with the Trio section heard twice. The finale has something of the character of a *perpetuum mobile* – the kind of movement based on continuously running fast notes more common in solo instrumental music. Much of this movement's ebullient wit and humour derives from the way Beethoven distributes the running semiquaver patterns around the orchestra: the brief but tongue-twisting bassoon solo at the beginning of the recapitulation (bb184–7) –

[2] Lewis Lockwood, *Beethoven: The Music and the Life* (New York, 2003), 215
[3] Robert Schumann, *On Music and Musicians* (New York, 1946), 99

ironically marked *dolce* – is a particularly delicious example. Near the end of the movement the main theme halves its speed and the dialogue becomes momentarily more reflective (bb345–350). But it is only momentary; the spirit of comedy prevails in the end.

Stephen Johnson

Vorwort

dem Grafen Franz von Oppersdorf gewidmet
komponiert: 1806 in Wien
Uraufführung: März 1807 in der Wohnung des Fürsten Lobkowitz;
erste öffentliche Aufführung am 15. November 1807 im Wiener Burgtheater
Originalverlag: Bureau des Arts et d'Industrie, Wien und Pest, 1809;
erste Partiturausgabe bei Simrock, 1823
Orchesterbesetzung: Flöte, 2 Oboen, 2 Klarinetten, 2 Fagotte – 2 Hörner,
2 Trompeten – Pauken – Streicher
Spieldauer: etwa 35 Minuten

Beethoven komponierte seine 4. Sinfonie in einer außergewöhnlich produktiven Schaffens-
phase. Nachdem er 1804 die *Eroica*-Sinfonie (Nr. 3) vollendet hatte, begann er Ideen zu
notieren, die später in die 5. Sinfonie (c-Moll) und in die 6. Sinfonie (*Pastorale*) einfließen
sollten. Aber Beethoven schien erkannt zu haben, dass diese Samen noch Zeit zum Keimen
brauchen würden. Während die meisten Komponisten ihre Aufmerksamkeit nun weniger
anspruchsvollen Dingen zugewendet hätten, beschloss Beethoven, sich mit einer weiteren
Sinfonie zu beschäftigen. Das sich daraus ergebende Werk, 1808 als Sinfonie Nr. 4 in B-Dur
veröffentlicht, scheint innerhalb kurzer Zeit entstanden zu sein, vermutlich im Juli/August
1806 – also während einer Pause von der Komposition der drei *Rasumowski*-Quartette,
op. 59. Im großen Gegensatz zu den Sinfonien Nr. 3, 5 und 6, die alle sehr ausführlich
skizziert wurden, sind für die Sinfonie Nr. 4 kaum Skizzen überliefert, woraus einige
Beethoven-Kenner geschlossen haben, dass Beethoven wahrscheinlich ziemlich bald mit der
Arbeit an der Dirigierpartitur angefangen hat.[1]

Die vergleichsweise einfache Konzeption und Entstehung der 4. Sinfonie hat zu der weit ver-
breiteten Ansicht geführt, dass sie nach der kühnen Originalität der *Eroica* eine Entspannung
oder sogar einen Rückschritt darstellt. Ein oberflächlicher Blick auf die Partitur würde dazu
führen, diese Sichtweise zu bestätigen. Hatten die 3. und die 5. Sinfonie die Ausdruckskraft
des Orchesters Anfang des 19. Jahrhunderts wie nie zuvor verbessert, scheint die 4. Sinfonie
insgesamt klassischer zu sein. Sie ist für das kleinste Orchester instrumentiert, das Beethoven
jemals in einer Sinfonie verwendet hat: nur eine Flöte, jeweils zwei Oboen, Klarinetten,
Fagotte, Hörner, Trompeten sowie Pauken und die üblichen Streicher. Die *Eroica* und die
Sinfonie in c-Moll weisen beide mutige formale Neuerungen auf: zum Beispiel die Ver-

---

[1] Siehe zum Beispiel: Barry Cooper: Einleitung zu Beethovens Symphonie Nr. 4 in B-Dur, Kassel 2001, S. IX.

bindung von Variation und Sonatenform im Finale der *Eroica* oder der großartige, allmählich zunehmende Übergang zwischen dem Scherzo und dem Finale in der 5. Sinfonie. Die 4. Sinfonie kommt dahingegen mit den übernommenen klassischen Abläufen weitgehend aus.

Wenn man jedoch etwas genauer hinsieht, wird die Originalität und Feinheit der 4. Sinfonie deutlich. Der Beethoven-Forscher Lewis Lockwood lobte diese Sinfonie, da sie „den Eindruck eines göttlichen Spiels unter fein ausbalancierten Kräften"[2] vermittelt, der Komponist Robert Schumann bezeichnete sie als Beethovens „griechisch-schlanke"[3] Sinfonie. Die 4. Sinfonie zeichnet wie die 5. Sinfonie einen Verlauf von der Dunkelheit ins Helle vor, obwohl hier das überwältigende Hervortreten ins Sonnenlicht viel früher geschieht. Die langsame Einleitung steht in der düsteren Tonart b-Moll. Zuerst erklingt ein anhaltendes, gedämpftes Unisono in mehreren Oktaven (Bläser) mit langsam absteigenden Terzen in den Streichern. Dies ist zweimal zu hören, anschließend tasten zaghafte Violinfiguren nach neuen Tonarten (Takt 18 usw.). Danach wiederholen die Violinen nur eine Note, Crescendo (Takt 35), und eine erbittert wiederholte Geste des gesamten Orchesters im Fortissimo führt uns direkt ins Allegro vivace und die Durtonart.

Nachdem die Dunkelheit vertrieben ist, beginnt das „göttliche Spiel". Etwas vom dialogorientierten Geist der klassischen Kammermusik dringt in die Schreibweise des ersten Satzes ein, mit lebhaften Dialogen der Holzbläser und Streicher. Der originellste Moment erscheint direkt vor der Wiederkehr des ersten Themas aus dem Allegro. Der energiegeladene Durchführungsteil scheint von einem dissonanten Akkord (Takt 261) „aufgespießt" zu werden, der sich dann in gedämpften Fragmenten der sich abwechselnden ersten und zweiten Violinen auflöst: erst staccato, dann legato. Dies führt in einen Fis-Dur-Septakkord (Takt 281) im *ppp* – eine extreme Dynamik zu jener Zeit; die Pauken bleiben jedoch leise in B (enharmonisch Ais, die Terz von Fis). Der Streicherklang wechselt dann in B-Dur, Tonika 6-4 (Takt 305), und ein langes Crescendo führt triumphierend zur Wiederkehr des ersten Themas (Takt 337).

Vieles von der Dramatik im Adagio der 4. Sinfonie ist auf die Interaktion und den Kontrast zwischen den liedartigen Melodien und den martialischen Rhythmen zurückzuführen. Die Präsenz des Marschelementes macht sich in den zweiten Violinen mit einem sehr einprägsamen punktierten Rhythmus auf zwei Noten sofort bemerkbar. Die folgende langatmige Melodie der ersten Violinen verbannt nicht die Erinnerung an diesen Rhythmus (Andeutungen setzen sich in den tieferen Streichern fort); am Höhepunkt der Melodie kommt er wieder zum Vorschein, nun kraftvoll betont von den Trompeten und Pauken (Takt 9). Im Herzen des Adagios gibt es einen besonders poetischen Moment. Nach dem sorgenvollen zentralen Höhepunkt des Satzes scheinen die Violinen auf einem einzigen mehrdeutigen ruhigen Akkord stehen zu bleiben (Takt 54 ff.) – wie in der bemerkenswerten gedämpften Passage im ersten Satz. Die martialische Figur flackert im hohen Fagott auf, eine Klarinette

---

[2] Lewis Lockwood: *Beethoven. Seine Musik. Sein Leben*, Kassel 2009, S. 168.
[3] Robert Schumann: *Gesammelte Schriften über Musik und Musiker*, Wiesbaden o. J., S. 18

klagt sanft – dann erscheint ein anderer Moment des Sonnenlichts, als die Hörner, Pauken und die Flöte den Satz mühelos in die Reprise führen (Takt 64).

Es gibt eine deutliche Neuerung im folgenden Scherzo: Statt des klassischen A–B–A-Schemas (das vom Menuett übernommen wurde) nimmt uns Beethoven auf eine A–B–A–B–A-Rundreise mit, bei dem der Trio-Abschnitt zweimal erscheint. Das Finale hat den Charakter eines Perpetuum mobile – der Satz basiert auf kontinuierlich durchlaufenden schnellen Noten, was man eher aus der instrumentalen Solomusik kennt. Vieles von dem überschwänglichen Witz und Humor dieses Satzes lässt sich davon ableiten, wie Beethoven die durchlaufenden Sechzehntelmuster um das Orchester herum verteilt: Das kurze, aber zungenbrecherische Fagott-Solo zu Beginn der Reprise (Takte 184–187) – das ironischerweise mit *dolce* bezeichnet ist – ist ein besonders gutes Beispiel hierfür. Gegen Ende des Satzes wird das Tempo des Hauptthemas halb so langsam und der Dialog wird kurzzeitig etwas nachdenklicher (Takte 345–350). Aber das ist nur vorübergehend; der Geist der Komödie setzt sich am Ende durch.

Stephen Johnson
Übersetzung: Uta Pastowski

Symphony No. 4

À Monsieur le Comte d'Oppersdorf

Ludwig van Beethoven
(1770–1827)
Op. 60

EAS 187

Edited by Richard Clarke
© 2014 Ernst Eulenburg Ltd, London
and Ernst Eulenburg & Co GmbH, Mainz

2

4

Allegro vivace ($\circ = 80$)

6

10

14

18

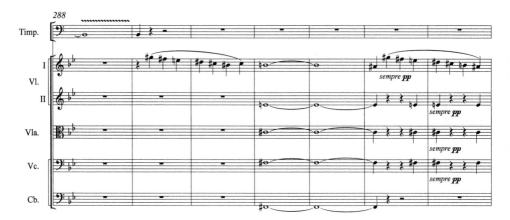

28

EAS 187

30

32

33

II. **Adagio** (♪ = 84)

EAS 187

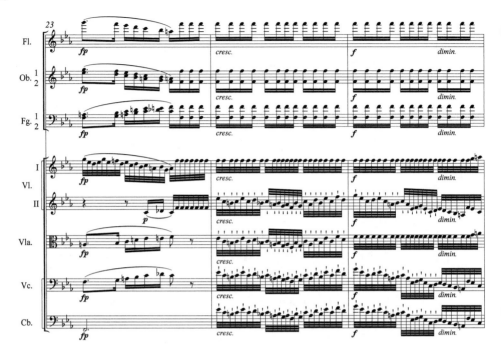

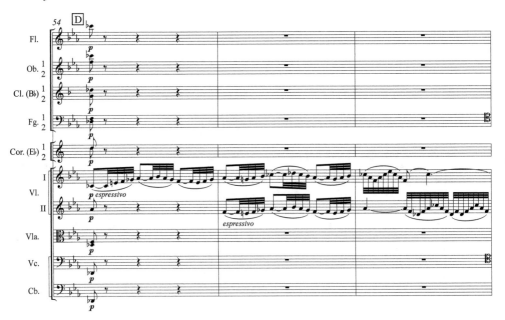

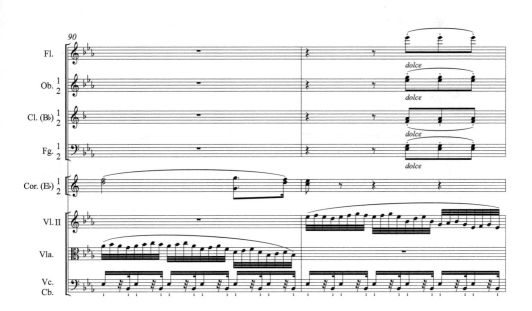

46

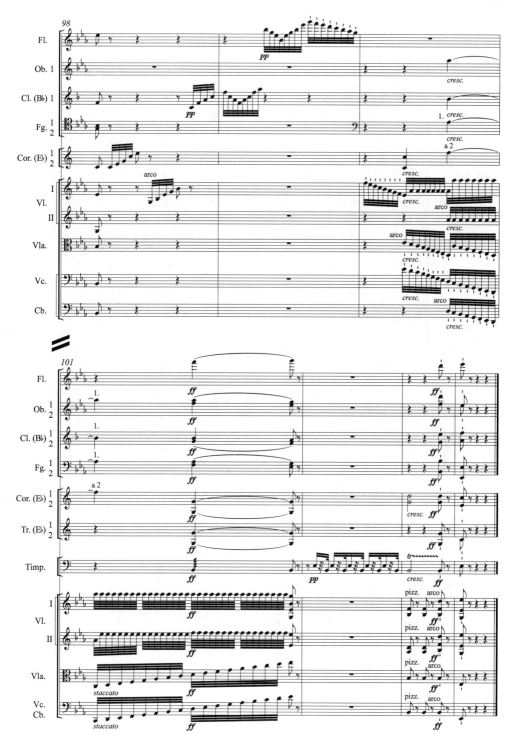

48

III. Menuetto

Allegro vivace ($\quad \! . = 100$)

Trio

Un poco meno Allegro ($\s2. = 88$)

56

Tempo I ($\downarrow. = 100$)

58

64

EAS 187

Tempo I (♩. = 100)

IV. Allegro ma non troppo ($\downarrow$ = 80)

70

EAS 187

72

EAS 187

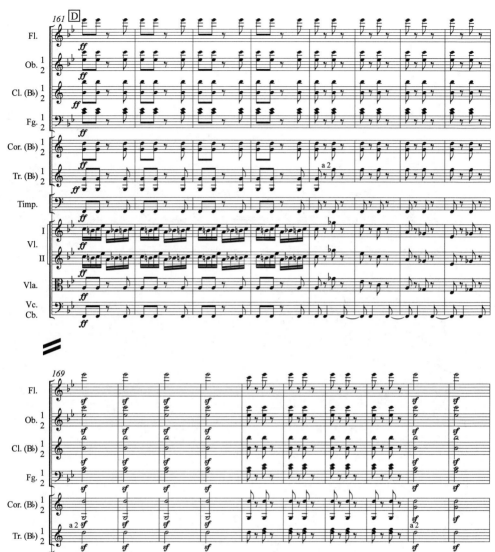

88

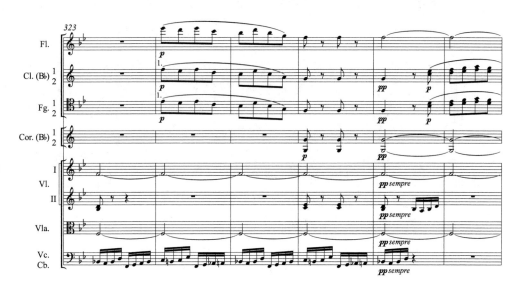

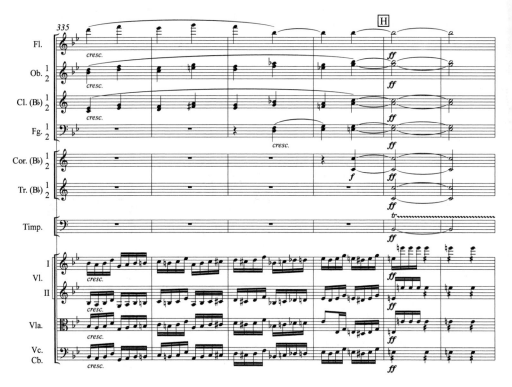

Printed in China